Darling Allan.
To many !
Of . . . . . :
eggs

HOW TO KEEP LA....... .....
AND TO
REAR CHICKENS

loves
Lisa
X X XX

IN LARGE OR SMALL NUMBERS, IN ABSOLUTE
CONFINEMENT, EMBRACING THE INTENSIVE

AND SEMI-INTENSIVE SYSTEMS

BY

W. M. ELKINGTON

AUTHOR OF "POPULAR POULTRY KEEPING,"

"EGG AND POULTRY RAISING AT HOME." ETC.

Welcome to our
new home — my
Lord Whitehall,
all my love
Lady Whitehall
xxx

British Library Cataloguing-in-Publication Data
A catalogue record for this book is available from the
British Library

Contents

Poultry Farming

Poultry farming is the raising of domesticated birds such as chickens, turkeys, ducks, and geese, for the purpose of farming meat or eggs for food. Poultry are farmed in great numbers with chickens being the most numerous. More than 50 billion chickens are raised annually as a source of food, for both their meat and their eggs. Chickens raised for eggs are usually called 'layers' while chickens raised for meat are often called 'broilers'. In total, the UK alone consumes over 29 million eggs per day

According to the Worldwatch Institute, 74% of the world's poultry meat, and 68% of eggs are produced in ways that are described as 'intensive'. One alternative to intensive poultry farming is free-range farming using much lower stocking densities. This type of farming allows chickens to roam freely for a period of the day, although they are usually confined in sheds at night to protect them from predators or kept indoors if the weather is particularly bad. In the UK, the Department for Environment, Food and Rural Affairs (Defra) states that a free-range chicken must have day-time access to open-air runs during at least half of its life. Thankfully, free-range farming of egg-laying hens is increasing its share of the market. Defra figures indicate that

45% of eggs produced in the UK throughout 2010 were free-range, 5% were produced in barn systems and 50% from cages. This compares with 41% being free-range in 2009. Despite this increase, unfortunately most birds are still reared and bred in 'intensive' conditions. Commercial hens usually begin laying eggs at 16–20 weeks of age, although production gradually declines soon after from approximately 25 weeks of age. This means that in many countries, by approximately 72 weeks of age, flocks are considered economically unviable and are slaughtered after approximately 12 months of egg production. This is despite the fact that chickens will naturally live for 6 or more years. In some countries, hens are 'force molted' to re-invigorate egg-laying. This practice is performed on a large commercial scale by artificially provoking a complete flock of hens to molt simultaneously. This is usually achieved by withdrawal of feed for 7-14 days which has the effect of allowing the hen's reproductive tracts to regress and rejuvenate. After a molt, the hen's production rate usually peaks slightly below the previous peak rate and egg quality is improved. In the UK, the Department for Environment, Food and Rural Affairs states 'In no circumstances may birds be induced to moult by withholding feed and water.' Sadly, this is not the case in all countries however.

Other practices in chicken farming include 'beak trimming', this involves cutting the hen's beak when they are born, to reduce the damaging effects of aggression, feather pecking and cannibalism. Scientific studies have shown that such practices are likely to cause both acute and chronic pain though, as the beak is a complex, functional organ with an extensive nervous supply. Behavioural evidence of pain after beak trimming in layer hen chicks has been based on the observed reduction in pecking behaviour, reduced activity and social behaviour, and increased sleep duration. Modern egg laying breeds also frequently suffer from osteoporosis which results in the chicken's skeletal system being weakened. During egg production, large amounts of calcium are transferred from bones to create egg-shell. Although dietary calcium levels are adequate, absorption of dietary calcium is not always sufficient, given the intensity of production, to fully replenish bone calcium. This can lead to increases in bone breakages, particularly when the hens are being removed from cages at the end of laying.

The majority of hens in many countries are reared in battery cages, although the European Union Council Directive 1999/74/EC has banned the conventional battery cage in EU states from January 2012. These are small cages, usually made of metal in modern systems, housing 3 to 8 hens. The walls are made of either solid metal or mesh, and the floor is sloped wire mesh to allow the faeces to drop through and eggs to roll onto an egg-collecting conveyor belt. Water is usually provided by overhead nipple systems, and food in a trough along the front of the cage replenished at regular intervals by a mechanical chain. The cages are arranged in long rows as multiple tiers, often with cages back-to-back (hence the term 'battery cage'). Within a single shed, there may be several floors contain battery cages meaning that a single shed may contain many tens of thousands of hens. In response to tightened legislation, development of prototype commercial furnished cage systems began in the 1980s. Furnished cages, sometimes called 'enriched' or 'modified' cages, are cages for egg laying hens which have been designed to overcome some of the welfare concerns of battery cages whilst retaining their economic and husbandry advantages, and also provide some of the welfare advantages of non-cage systems.

Many design features of furnished cages have been incorporated because research in animal welfare science has shown them to be of benefit to the hens. In the UK, the Defra 'Code for the Welfare of Laying Hens' states furnished cages should provide at least 750 cm2 of cage area per hen, 600 cm2 of which should be usable; the height of the cage other than that above the usable area should be at least 20 cm at every point and no cage should have a total area that is less than 2000 cm2. In addition, furnished cages should provide a nest, litter such that pecking and scratching are possible, appropriate perches allowing at least 15 cm per hen, a claw-shortening device, and a feed trough which may be used without restriction providing 12 cm per hen. The practice of chicken farming continues to be a much debated area, and it is hoped that in this increasingly globalised and environmentally aware age, the inhumane side of chicken farming will cease. There are many thousands of chicken farms (and individual keepers) that treat their chickens with the requisite care and attention, and thankfully, these numbers are increasing.

CHAPTER I

ACCOMMODATION

THE first edition of this book was written many years ago by the late Major Morant, who was one of the first to discover the possibilities of keeping hens in close confinement. Then, before the first great war, the present author re-wrote the book in the light of the progress that had since been made in the breeding and management of productive poultry. Now, after the toll of a second great war, when our sources of egg supply are seriously reduced, and despite the various obstacles, more and more people are thinking of keeping a few hens in a garden or backyard, it has been brought up to date so that it may serve as a guide to the many thousands who are keeping their own few fowls as the best means of producing eggs from materials which would be regarded as waste under peace conditions.

This present edition is necessitated by the fact that the methods of feeding poultry have undergone revolutionary changes. The grain mixtures and mashes with which we regaled our stock in ordinary times hav disappeared, and the poultry-keeper must exercise some ingenuity in improvising foods—on which account the subsequent chapter on feeding and management has been rewritten.

When previous editions of this book were written its appeal was limited to those who liked keeping poultry as a hobby, and others who hoped to make profit—as many did. In these days the great incentive is the production of food, particularly production of human food out of materials which could not be employed to better purpose. We are denied the use of grains and meals such as are given to poultry normally, for the reason that these are reserved for human consumption, or for stock rated higher than the domestic hen. Happily, the hen is the most adaptable of all domestic livestock and least likely to resent substitute rations. Her owner or attendant, however, has a more difficult task, for instead of being able to run to the corn merchant for grain and meal he must improvise rations according to his enterprise and industry. If he has registered under the Domestic Poultry-keepers scheme he will be allowed a certain proportion of balancer meal, which will not be enough to maintain his stock, but will provide something in the nature of balanced proportions of protein, carbohydrates and other elements to add to whatever bulk food he may secure.

The problems of feeding will be dealt with more fully in another chapter. For the present we must consider the conditions under which the hens are to be kept. Among present small poultry-keepers we find some with almost unlimited range, others who want to keep a few fowls in a garden of limited extent, and many more who have nothing better than a town backyard. And lest the last-named may despair of their chances, let us say that some of the most painstaking—and therefore successful—poultry-keepers we have come across have been of the backyarder class. They could only find room for a small intensive house or scratching-shed, and everything depended on their personal care. Of course, those who were neglectful speedily came to grief; but the enthusiasts surprised themselves and their friends by the number of eggs they produced—even in winter.

When Major Morant wrote the first edition of this book little was known about the capacity of hens to lay in winter. Many people, indeed, thought winter was a close season for egg-production; whereas in recent years we have proved that, by good breeding, by good management and housing, by good feeding and by hatching at the right time, we could get eggs from October to February almost as freely as from February onward. From the small poultry-keeper's point of view the intensive house or scratching-shed is the main factor—provided the stock are of the right class and of the right age, for the reason that the birds are under cover and sheltered from rain and cold wind, and they have a dry littered floor on which to scratch.

However, the intensive or scratching-shed system may not suit all circumstances, so I propose to detail the various methods of accommodating poultry, with their particular advantages and drawbacks, so that everyone may decide which will suit him best. If you are fortunate enough to have a good-sized paddock or orchard in which to run your poultry you can adopt any type of house, though the most suitable and economical would be a portable structure that could be moved on to fresh ground as required. But a housing system that is well suited for the farm or small-holding, where it is desirable to move the stock and spread their manure, is not necessarily suited to the conditions of a back garden.

It is presumed that the majority of those who read this book have very limited space for poultry. Even if they have a good-sized garden they will not want to devote much of it to poultry; and on no account should hens—or even growing chicks—be allowed to run at large in a garden. They must be confined in some way, and their housing must conform to the limitations of their range. That is why the intensive or semi-intensive systems are advantageous. By intensive is meant permanent close confinement to a scratching-shed, whereas semi-intensive implies the use of a small outside run for use when the weather is favourable. But do not exaggerate the importance of this outside run. If of very limited extent it will soon be worn bare of grass, so that its usefulness for exercise is questionable, except, perhaps, in summer, when the hens can dust themselves in the dry earth. But that small space would render much more service if it were covered over and converted into a scratching-shed, in which the fowls could scratch and keep fit and well in all weathers.

This principle of covering a limited space, thereby using it to the best advantage, is illustrated in Fig. 1.

This introduces the permanent semi-open front, and many people are astonished, when they see this building for the first time, to learn that the hens roost inside it without any further protection. This is rendered possible by the depth of the building from back to front. The house illustrated is 6ft. across the front and 9ft. deep. The perch, it will be seen, is fixed at the back, and fairly high up, whilst the roof projects 18in. in the front, thus providing considerable protection from rain and wind, so that the hens roosting at the back are out of reach of wind and draughts, except in very exposed localities or where an unfavourable aspect has to be adopted, in which cases it is advisable to make use of sliding up-and-down glazed shutters, so that the front may be covered when necessary, with the exception of about 6in. at the top. A south aspect should be chosen for houses of this kind whenever possible, and in the majority of cases, unless there is much exposure to high winds, it will be found that the birds will be quite comfortable at night without any additional protection than that afforded by the projecting roof and the deep, narrow building. The height of the house illustrated is 6ft. at the gable and 5ft. at the eaves, the front being boarded up 3ft. high, with wire netting above. This detail need not be carried out exactly to the letter, and a height of 4ft. at the eaves can be made to suffice if the open space in the front is in proportion. In order to afford good lighting at the back and under the droppings-board, it is advisable to put in a 2ft. square window on one side, if not on both. The interior arrangements are very simple, as shown, the nest-boxes being attached to the low front wall, whilst a droppings-board is hung beneath the perch, ensuring greater convenience in cleaning out and preventing the litter on the scratching floor being soiled by night droppings. A dozen or fourteen hens will be a convenient flock for a house of this extent, and, of course, buildings of any extent may be constructed on the same design, so long as one has plenty of depth in proportion to the length.

FIG. 1.—AN OPEN-FRONTED SCRATCHING-SHED HOUSE.

In some gardens we see a small poultry house with a covered run, enclosed all round with nothing but wire netting, with the consequence that rain beats in, the birds are exposed to cold winds and the litter (if any) is always getting wet. This is really wasting a good opportunity by false economy, for if the sides were closed in, with light and air apertures in front, the covered run would be dry, comfortable and serviceable in all weathers.

Another type of house, for those who want to occupy a strip of ground at the bottom of a garden, up against a wall or fence, is shown in Fig. 2. This conforms more to the popular idea of poultry-house construction, having roosting accommodation separate from the covered run. This may involve some waste of scratching floor-space, but on a long shallow strip of ground (this building covers 15ft. by 6ft.) it is impossible to accommodate hens on a perch at the back, even if the roof projects considerably more in front than is shown in the illustration. High winds search a long shallow building such as this, so that the best plan is to partition off 4ft. at one end as the roosting quarters, leaving 6in. of permanent ventilation at the top, and providing a sliding up-and-down shutter for use in the daytime. This will leave a covered run of lift, by 6ft., or 66 square feet, which will comfortably accommodate a dozen or fifteen hens. The arrangements are simple, but we advocate at least a foot of roof projection in front.

FIG. 2.—A LEAN-TO SCRATCHING-SHED, COMBIN-ING HOUSE AND RUN.

The provision of a hard brick, board, or concrete floor for an intensive house or a scratching-shed is by no means a matter of necessity. Such floors are easier to clean out, but their use is optional, and for our own part we have always been content with well-rammed earth, and if rats have been troublesome we have got over the difficulty by sinking small-meshed wire netting 18in. into the ground all round the building. With regard to litter, the best material is peat moss, which, on account of its absorbent qualities, lasts a long time; but as the cost is rather high, many people who have facilities for obtaining dried bracken tops, dried leaves, or broken packing straw will find it more economical to use those materials. Litter should be spread to a depth of 8in. to 12in., and a good way to go to work in a 6ft. by 9ft. house is to spread a barrow-load of dry sand or fine ashes, then a barrow-load of peat moss, with a bolting of broken straw over all. This will not need cleaning out more than once a quarter, and when a good depth of peat moss is used it will last for six months.

A third type of intensive house is shown in Fig. 3. This is a small, portable type suitable for a lawn or small area.

It is 7ft. long, 3ft. 6in. wide, and 3ft. high to the eaves, so that it provides 24 square feet of floor-space. There are ample light and ventilation in front and at one end, but these spaces are fitted with adjustable glazed shutters, so that in very severe weather a small opening at one end will admit sufficient air at night. The roof, which slides either way to allow access for collecting the eggs or cleaning out the building, has two hinged flaps, which may be raised and adjusted at any angle, these being supplemented by an inner roof of wire netting and canvas to provide air and shade in warm weather. The interior arrangements are not shown in the illustration Fig. 3, but there is a perch at the far end, with a droppings-board underneath, fixed about 18in. above the floor, whilst a couple of nest-boxes are fixed to the back wall at about the same height, together with food-trough, water-fountain, &c. The conditions might be improved somewhat by making the house a foot higher and raising the perch and nest-boxes another 6in., and, of course, houses of the same design may be made of larger or even smaller dimensions.

FIG. 3.—A SMALL INTENSIVE HOUSE.

A few comments are necessary about floor space in intensive houses. It has been claimed that two square feet per bird is quite sufficient for laying hens; but in actual practice this is running it too fine, and we prefer to err on the side of generosity. In the small portable intensive house we have just described as being suitable for half a dozen hens the space runs to 4 square feet per bird, while in the house shown in Fig. 1 fourteen hens enjoy the same proportion of floor space. So we advise you to apportion floor space on this basis. And don't forget that you can economise floor space by putting a wide board under the perches to catch droppings, so that if there is sufficient head room under the droppings board, and sufficient light to enable the birds to see to scratch there, you can count that as floor space. As for perching space, you can allow 8in., to 9in. for heavy breed hens and 7in. for light breeds like Leghorns.

We must now describe two types of housing suitable for the garden. One is known as the fold house, consisting of a small roosting house, just big enough for the required number of birds, with a fixed wired run. The entire contrivance may be mounted on a pair of wheels at one end, and have handles at the other, so that two persons—or even one—can move it a few yards. For convenience in the smaller gardens the wired run may be separate, being fastened on to the house by hooks and hasps. The idea of this type of housing is to enable different parts of the garden to be covered. In the summer growing season the cultivated ground may be under crops, so the fold will have to be confined to the lawn; but at other times it is beneficial to move the fold on to ground from which crops have been taken. The hens may find some food, and they will give the land a dressing of manure. The fold can be left on the same spot for two or three days, and then be moved a few yards to fresh ground.

Another method of letting your hens fertilise your garden, is to have a small portable house (the type shown in Fig. 3 will suffice) with a few hurdles covered with wire netting to enclose a small space of ground not under crop. The hurdles are easily pulled up and driven in again, the house can be carried or dragged a few yards; and so we are able to put our hens on to a bit of fresh ground every few days, and at the same time provide rich manure for future crops. In this connection we would stress the importance of slatted floors to folds and small houses that are to be moved about the garden. The slats—about an inch across and an inch between each, allow night droppings to fall through; and with an occasional scraping they can be kept quite clean. But remember that slatted floors are essentially for portable houses, for the better distribution of manure; and they must not be introduced into intensive houses or scratching-sheds.

In ordinary times we would have made reference to the most modern method of housing laying hens—in battery cages. Though it may seem cruel to confine a hen in a cage 18 inches square this system made great progress before the war. But because these closely confined birds need a special diet it would be unwise to venture upon such a system without necessary resources and more than an elementary knowledge of poultry management.

CHAPTER II

BREED AND STRAIN

ONE of the most potent factors in the development of the poultry industry has been the creation and improvement of certain strains or families in various breeds for the express purpose of economical production. It is one of the essential facts which the poultry-keeping tyro needs to get fixed in his mind, for the success of his operations depends to a very large extent upon the class of stock he keeps. It is only within recent years that any considerable number of poultry-keepers have worked upon the principle that productive and economic traits can be influenced and governed by careful selection of breeding stock. We do not need to go far back into the last century to find the majority of so-called utility poultry-keepers mainly dependent for pure-bred stock upon the cast-offs from fanciers' yards, and in those days people spoke of the utility merits of this breed and that as if commercial usefulness was a natural breed trait the same as colour or shape or comb formation.

Nowadays we adopt the principle that economic productiveness is not a question of breed, but of strain—not a natural trait, but a cultivated one. And the fact upon which we may congratulate ourselves is that since this principle has been recognised breeders have made very substantial headway in breeding useful traits into certain strains. When the Utility Poultry Club organised its first laying competition, which ran for sixteen weeks in the winter of 1897-98, the winning pen of four pullets produced 161 eggs; but so successfully did these events stimulate public interest in cultivating winter egg-production that in 1911-12 the winning pen score by four pullets in sixteen winter weeks was 324 eggs. To-day one occasionally hears of individual birds laying upwards of 280 eggs in a year, though these are isolated instances, and the records are less striking and less significant than flock averages of from 200 to 220 eggs per annum from fifty or sixty hens.

At any rate, the lesson to be gleaned is that productiveness is a cultivated trait, and that being the case, it is obviously to the advantage of everyone who keeps fowls to cultivate it to the extent of his ability, and in any case to differentiate between strains or families that have been bred strictly on utility lines and those which have not. In all the popular varieties one will find strains of widely-varying character. Take the Rhode Island Red, for example. There are many useful strains that have been "bred to lay," as the saying is; others that have been cultivated mainly for exhibition properties, and, being much larger birds, are less economical, though they may be fairly good layers; besides many more strains, if they may be so termed, which, though pure bred, have never been selected and bred on systematic lines for the development of useful characters.

In order more thoroughly to appreciate the meaning of strain it is necessary to view it in the right perspective, and we do not want anyone to imagine that so long as he keeps stock descended from a strain that has actually been bred to lay, they may be depended upon to yield eggs in all seasons, regardless of the manner in which the birds are housed, fed, and managed. That would be a very mischievous idea, for environment has a more powerful *direct* influence upon production than anything else. Consequently, however well bred one's hens might be, and however successfully the trait of productiveness may have been cultivated, the birds would not acquit themselves creditably if the housing arrangements and general management were unfavourable. Moreover, favourable housing and management conditions would most likely coax eggs from hens that did not actually inherit laying character. But given equally satisfactory environment, it is very certain that the hens which have inherited laying capacity will yield infinitely better results, and as they will cost no more to rear and to feed (probably not so much), there is a very good reason why everyone who takes up egg-production, either as a profitable hobby or as a business, should make a particular point of keeping stock of a genuine utility "bred to lay" strain.

But though strain should be the first consideration in selecting stock, breed characteristics are sufficiently distinctive to justify some care in picking out varieties that are most likely to give satisfactory results under certain conditions. We do not propose to describe the hundred or more breeds and sub-varieties of pure poultry, for the excellent reason that many are of no practical value to those who are interested in egg-production, so we shall content ourselves by referring to those most worthy of notice, particularly those to which creators of the modern laying strains have paid special attention. In this connection we should like to explain that the popularity of certain breeds, such as the Rhode Island Red and the White Leghorn, is not due so much to their natural qualities as to the fact that they were among the first to receive attention from specialist breeders, as we call the skilled developers of laying strains, and they have on that account unquestionably acquitted themselves in public and private tests more creditably than any other breeds. In course of time thay may be equalled and possibly superseded by varieties which, in our opinion, possess equally good natural qualifications, and only await equally careful development at the hands of the specialists; but at the present time there can be no doubt that Rhode Island Reds and White Leghorns occupy pride of place among egg-producing breeds.

These two varieties, however, represent two distinct classes of poultry, commonly known as heavy and light, or sitters and non-sitters. The heavy breeds are possessed of larger, heavier bodies, they are addicted to broodiness more or less frequently, especially in spring and summer, and they lay brown or tinted eggs; whereas the light breeds have much smaller bodies, their eggs are white, and they very seldom become broody, this natural instinct having been almost bred out by years of selection, although occasionally one comes across a reversion to type, and instances of broodiness among so-called non-sitting varieties by no means imply impurity of breed.

Taking the two classes on the whole, it may be said that the light breeds lack table properties, as they carry comparatively little flesh, but they are more economical to rear and maintain, and they are quite as prolific as the heavy breeds, and probably more so in spring and summer. Their hardiness has sometimes been disputed, and it cannot be doubted that in an exposed position the light breeds are not likely to yield such good returns in winter, though it must be noted that in the modern laying strains hardiness has been carefully cultivated, and some of the most notable returns in winter-laying contests, including the 324-egg score by four pullets in sixteen weeks, have been credited to White Leghorns, whilst under favourable covered run conditions the light breeds are under no handicap whatever, however severe the weather may be.

Naturally, we find the best table poultry among the heavy breeds, and this section may be sub-divided in order to group separately those in which laying properties rank before table qualities, and *vice versa*. We should class the Rhode Island Red as a variety in which laying traits are of more value than table properties, and Buff Plymouth Rocks and White Wyandottes might be included in the same category, as also might Buff Orpingtons. On the other hand, table properties are of more consequence in Sussex and Faverolles, which are also good layers. At any rate, if we were selecting a heavy breed expressly for egg-production, we should choose the Rhode Island Red; if we wanted a prime table breed that was also a good layer we should select one of the Sussex varieties—either the Light, Speckled, or Red; and if we wanted to strike the happy medium and combine both properties as nearly as possible in the one breed we should choose either the Rhode Island Red or the Buff Rock.

Turning to the light breeds, we favour first of all the White Leghorn, then the Black Leghorn, the Ancona, and the Brown Leghorn. The Campine alone can make any pretence to table qualities, for it has a long breast, carrying a nice lot of flesh, and the surplus cockerels come in handy for home consumption and are readily marketable as spring chickens at an early age. This is a Belgian variety that will be more popular when its laying properties have been developed on pedigree lines, for no other light breed can as yet compete with the White Leghorn in that respect. Once upon a time the Minorca was regarded as one of the best laying breeds, and it certainly won the first laying competition. We have found it very useful in sheltered quarters, but its hardiness is open to question, and specialist breeders of heavy layers have scarcely given it any attention, so that we should not in these days recommend it as one of the most valuable laying breeds. There are many other breeds of useful character, as well as additional sub-varieties of the breeds already mentioned; but our reason for mentioning only a few is to be found in the fact that we are most anxious to impress the importance of keeping stock of the best bred-to-lay strains, and such strains are only to be found in a limited number of breeds, including those to which we have referred. Therefore, we beg our readers to note that, although we have expressed a preference for certain breeds, the final choice should be one of strain. It may, for instance, be decided to keep Rhode Island Reds, but unless the stock is obtained from a strain in which productive and economic traits have been specially cultivated, disappointment is likely to be experienced; for even in this popular breed there are many families in which systematic breeding has never been practised, and others in which show properties have been cultivated at the expense of useful ones, so that for commercial purposes members of these families are very little if any better than the chance-bred nondescripts of the farmyard.

Now let us explain how these productive strains are created, and how they can be maintained. First of all we must bear in mind the important fact that all economic properties are dependent upon vigour, vitality, energy, stamina, or whatever the poultry-keeper chooses to call it. When vitality or stamina is lost it will be found impossible to retain economic traits, and it should be understood that this essential condition may be sacrificed, not merely through sheer carelessness and permitting unhealthy and degenerate birds to interbreed, but also by selecting immature birds for stock purposes, or even those apparently useful birds whose energy or stamina has been reduced by precocity or a long spell of productiveness. Prolificacy being a cultivated trait and depending largely upon inheritance, it follows that the most useful birds of each generation should be selected for breeding purposes, in order that the trait may be perpetuated in the next and future generations. The principle of selection is, indeed, a most important and influential factor, and in order to make selection more certain the majority of breeders—and practically all the more successful ones—employ trap-nests, which confine the hen until the attendant releases her, identifies her by a numbered ring upon the leg, and registers her egg upon a chart, which provides a faithful record of production for every hen in the flock, and enables the manager to see at a glance at the end of a year or any shorter period what sort of productive character is borne by each and every hen in the flock. It may be possible for the owner of a small flock to watch the habits and get to know fairly accurately the character of each hen, so that he may weed out the poor layers and breed only from those with good records; but it is obvious that this would be impossible among a large flock, and in such cases trap-nests are essential to the success of pedigree breeding operations.

It must be understood that in every flock of laying hens there will be some whose records will exceed the average production of the whole flock, and others whose egg returns will be considerably below the average. This will be the case even among flocks descended from stock that have been trap-nested and bred on pedigree lines for generations, so it follows that the work of selection must go on year after year, and it is very little use buying a pen of well-bred birds or selecting breeding stock for one season only and expecting everything to go right afterwards. Of course, we are referring to cases where it is desired to build up prolific strains or to maintain them at a high level, and we do not wish small operators to imagine that all this labour is essential to success in their cases, though, as we have indicated, the selection of useful stock is a very important factor in egg-production.

In the foregoing remarks we have referred only to pure breeds; but in the inter-war commercial era there was an important development of cross breeding or first crossing. It has always been an elementary theory that by crossing two pure breeds one could combine the best features of each; but crossing may also result in aggravating serious defects, so we have to be careful. However, first crosses between cultivated pure breeds are now regarded as sound economy, and many amateurs may elect to try these first crosses, especially if pullets are offered at lower prices than the pure-breds. But let us emphasise the difference between genuine first crosses and mere mongrels, resulting from indiscriminate crossing, probably for several generations. The average mongrel is a degenerate, and you cannot expect much from her, whereas genuine first cross pullets should lay as well as pure-breds, especially if bred directly from selected specimens of two pure breeds.

Among popular first crosses are Rhode Island Red—Light Sussex, White Leghorn—White Wyandotte, Black Leghorn—Rhode Island Red. In fact, one can ring the changes among any good pure breeds as long as one selects good material for breeding. The most useful first crosses, however, are those carrying sex-linkage, as a result of which the sex of the chicks can be discerned at birth. Take the Rhode Island Red—Light Sussex cross as the most notable example. This cross of a golden male on silver females results in the male chicks inheriting the colour characteristics of the mothers, while the female chicks inherit the colour characteristics of the sire. Another example is the Black Leghorn—Barred Rock cross. The male chicks assume the colour characteristics of the Barred Rocks, while the female chicks resemble the Black Leghorn.

Sex linkage enables us to buy day-old pullets—a great economy in these days for those who have space only to rear a few pullets. But one can also buy day-old pullets of pure breeds, for the art of sexing chicks at birth has become a commercial reality.

In these days of enforced economy we recommend the plan of buying day-old chicks or older pullets for replacement, in which case we need not keep a male bird, which is quite unnecessary, and a source of waste and trouble, unless fertile eggs for hatching are required.

CHAPTER III

FEEDING AND MANAGEMENT

IN ordinary times it was considered that those amateur poultry-keepers who took the trouble to acquire good stock and to provide favourable environment, had nothing more to do than to feed regularly, which was an easy matter because they could go to their corn merchants and buy everything essential for the welfare of their hens. Before the last war feeding had become so simplified that we had no cause to trouble about suitability of the rations, since enterprising food merchants employed experts to concoct balanced meals, and for the rest we could buy any grain we liked. Now, unfortunately, the supplies of normal feeding stuffs are restricted, and feeding has become the most difficult problem of all.

Reference has already been made to the Domestic Poultry-keepers scheme promoted by the Ministry of Agriculture, through which small poultry-keepers are registered for the allocation of a ration known as balancer meal. Since the composition of this mash must vary from time to time, according to the materials available, it need only be said that Government authorities have done their best to supply the most suitable meal mixture obtainable. To qualify for this ration the poultry-keeper must register under the scheme, and he can obtain an application form from the local Food Office, or from the Ministry of Agriculture (D.P.K.), Africa House, Kingsway, London, W.C.2. When a ration card is issued to an applicant he can take it to his corn merchant, who will then supply rations according to the number of units authorized.

Under the Domestic Poultry Rationing Scheme, 4 lb. of poultry balancer meal per month is issued against each shell egg registration surrendered. Balancer meal is a compound specifically prepared for use with household and garden waste, and it has been worked out that this ration of balancer meal used together with the waste is sufficient to keep one laying hen in good condition. By arrangement with friends and neighbours willing to contribute their waste and shell egg registrations, additional balancer meal can, of course, be obtained—but the limit of shell egg registrations that can be surrendered for any one poultry keeper has been fixed at twenty-five. It can be seen, therefore, that the domestic poultry keeper must restrict his stock of birds to the number of shell egg registrations surrendered in his name, and it is well to note here that under this new scheme no extra rations of foodstuffs can be obtained merely by increasing the number of birds kept.

The Government, anxious that available foodstuffs should be used to the best possible advantage, have undertaken a great deal of research into domestic poultry keeping and the Domestic Poultry Keepers' Council offer valuable free technical advice through the various leaflets obtainable from the Ministry of Agriculture and Fisheries at the above address. Local Domestic Poultry Keepers' Clubs have been formed throughout the country, addresses of which can be obtained from any Food Office. The benefit of these clubs cannot be too strongly stressed.

The present ration of balancer meal is based on $2\frac{1}{4}$ oz. a day per bird, to which should be added $\frac{1}{2}$ pint of waste. If more than this quantity of balancer meal is used the consequences of running short before the end of the rationing period will have to be faced. Edible household and garden waste includes vegetables and root peelings, green vegetable leaves, bean-pods and pea-shells, runner beans, carrots, turnips, and parsnip-tops, artichokes, small potatoes, apple-cores, bacon and cheese rind, etc., and these should be minced or chopped up and thoroughly cooked in a minimum of water, or—as many poultry keepers prefer—steamed. Even in these days of rigid economy there *must* be scraps left over from meals, and plate scrapings. These should be added to the cooked waste—not re-cooked. Warnings sounded so often about saving bread have made many poultry keepers feel uneasy, but no harm is done if the qualification "unfit for further use in the home" can honestly be met.

We will assume, therefore, that each day we have a varying quantity of stale bread, together with cooked potatoes, greens, and various oddments. The bread must be scalded, and when the water has cooled and the surplus poured off the cooked vegetables and other soft matter should be added, while finally sufficient balancer meal should be added to make it up into a moist, crumbly mash. You can mix and knead this mash much better with the hand than with a spoon; and you should serve it in a basin or a trough, which should be large enough and long enough to enable all the birds to get round and feed at once.

It would hardly be thought necessary to warn that soap, soda, vinegar, rhubarb and foods containing salt in large amounts are harmful and should not be fed, but it pays to be extremely scrupulous about the contents of household waste. Coffee grounds and used tea-leaves, too, have little or no food value and should be regarded as unsuitable for feeding.

In the good old days, when we could buy our food from the corn merchant, it was customary to give half the daily feed in the form of grain, and the plan generally in vogue was to start the day with a small handful of grain per bird scattered among the litter, followed at midday by a generous feed of mash, with another feed of grain an hour before the birds went to roost. But very few people are able to get grain just now, and thousands of hens are living entirely on mash—and doing very well on it, too, which shows what an adaptable creature the hen is. The result is more work for to-day's poultry-keeper, for though some people mix enough mash in the morning—or in the evening—to last throughout the day, others prefer to mix fresh mash for each meal—that is, for breakfast as early as possible in the morning, for lunch about midday, and for supper an hour or so before roosting-time, which is generally when dusk is falling.

Some poultry-keepers have been brought up in the belief that grain is essential for the health and welfare of poultry. Even a few grains of torpedoed and kilndried wheat are better than nothing; so if your corn merchant can supply such material in addition to your ration of balancer mash you should use this by scattering it among the litter in the scratching shed in the morning. Grain, as a means of promoting exercise, is more essential for closely confined stock than for hens which are running out on a garden. But if all else fails, and you think that you must give grain, or some other dry food, try making biscuits out of your mixture of scraps and balancer meal, adding a little flour if available. Dry the mixture to something like the consistency of pastry, roll it out, cut it into squares or biscuit forms, and cook these till they are crisp and will break up into granulated form. The dust can be used in the mash, and the granulated pieces will provide the hens with something in the way of a dry food.

If you are unable to obtain household scraps the best alternatives for providing the bulk of the mash are potatoes, carrots, parsnips and artichokes. Cook these (the potatoes in their skins unless they are green and sprouted) until they are quite soft and can be mashed to pulp, when the balancer mash is added, and the mash is kneeded up as before stated. Many large poultry farmers are using potatoes and other roots to the extent of 50 per cent. of the daily feed; and it is surprising how hens like this vegetable mash, and thrive upon it. We never need despair of keeping hens alive, and in lay, while we have plenty of potatoes and just a bit of meal to make up an appetising mash.

It will be appreciated that the combination of gardening and poultry-keeping is a great economy in these days. The garden should provide a lot of food for your hens, and the hens will enable you, to some extent, to solve the manure problem. But when we are asked what crops can be grown for poultry in a garden of modest size we must exercise discretion. One needs an area of considerable extent to make it worth while growing a crop of wheat or oats, while the returns from a plot of ground devoted to such crops as haricot or other beans, peas, buckwheat and the like are not to be compared with the value of the root crops from the same area. That is why we always recommend potatoes, carrots, parsnips, artichokes, together with turnips and greens, as the best crops that can be grown for poultry in a garden of limited extent. Of course, if you find any peas or beans left after the main crop has been gathered these should be picked, dried and kibbled, to be added to whatever small supplies of grain you can get.

Apart from the bulk foods, and those of definitely productive value, we must remember that fowls consume a lot of green food. If they are at liberty they will eat grass or whatever herbage may be available; so when you keep laying hens in close confinement see that they have some green food every day. There is no difficulty about this in a garden, where cabbage or lettuce leaves are generally available; but if you cannot grow your own be sure to save such waste green food as may be available. As an alternative plan, go out and gather dandelion leaves or young grass; but do not let your hens go without green food. And if you have plenty to give tie it in a bunch and hang it within reach for the hens to peck at.

Here we would like to warn readers against the practice of throwing scraps of green food, vegetables and other materials into the run for the hens to peck over. It is a lazy, wasteful plan, as unfair to the hens as it is unsatisfactory to the poultry-keeper, for the hens do not get the full value from the food, most of which is wasted; so they do not lay.

Let all waste food be cooked and served as we have suggested, with the exception of fresh green food.

The other requirements of laying hens are grit, lime and water. Happily, there is no shortage of these, and your corn merchant will supply you with flint grit to assist in grinding the food in the gizzard, and oyster shell or limestone to shell the eggs; and these should be kept before the hens in a box. Finally, remember that hens consume a great quantity of water, so see that water vessels are replenished two or three times a day, and kept clean. See, also, that the troughs or vessels in which the food is served are kept clean; for though hens will eat most things when served up attractively their appetite may be spoiled by soured food.

The above is a general outline of feeding to-day; and as conditions vary considerably now it may be necessary or desirable to vary the methods. We know that for years to come there will be a scarcity of grain and meals, so that we must improvise as well as we can. But many of us realise that our present experiences will stand us in good stead in the future, when, though grains and meals may be available, we shall know that less costly materials will suffice to produce eggs.

CHAPTER IV

BREEDING AND REARING

ALTHOUGH the breeding and rearing of young stock in confinement are perfectly feasible, the advisability of devoting valuable space to this work needs to be considered from the point of view of convenience in every individual case. The small hen-keeper, whose stock consists of half-a-dozen or a dozen birds in an intensive house or scratching-shed, would hardly be justified in maintaining a cock-bird in order to renew his laying stock, and if his space is very limited it is open to question whether it will pay him even to buy eggs for hatching and rear his own chickens. As a rule, unless a particular hen is a very good layer or a useful breeder, it is inadvisable to retain layers longer than two seasons. The average hen yields most eggs in her first laying season, and after the second season the reduction is generally so marked as to justify filling her place with a younger, more productive bird; therefore it is a very good plan to renew half the laying stock every autumn, so that no hens are kept after the second laying season. The old birds may be disposed of in July or August, before they fall into moult, and whilst they are still plump enough for killing, especially if they have been fed generously for two or three weeks.

It is open for the small hen-keeper with little space and convenience to purchase the few pullets he requires, whereas those who desire to engage in breeding and have the necessary space and time to attend to the work may bring up the young stock on the close confinement plan, provided they have the necessary sheltered accommodation. It must, however, be understood that the cost of production is much heavier by this method, and in the majority of cases hardier and more vigorous birds can be raised on the free range system, which is also the most economical plan of raising young stock. Indeed, it has been admitted by some enthusiastic advocates of the intensive system that there is a considerable gain in keeping pullets that have been brought up on free range, such birds possessing more stamina, and the only question is whether the change from free range to close confinement is so great as to affect the productive habits of the pullets. Our experience is that the birds do suffer somewhat through the change, but it is only temporary, provided the confined conditions afford scope for exercise; and, on the whole, we consider the gain in stamina makes free range rearing preferable when it can be conveniently adopted.

Having already dealt with breeding principles, we need only add that matured hens (two or three years old) mated with vigorous yearling cockerels are likely to yield the best results.

A cockerel may run with eight or ten hens of a breed like the R. I. Red, and a dozen or fifteen of a light breed, but it is inadvisable to run two males in the same house with a larger flock of females. Stock should be mated up a month before fertile eggs are required for hatching, and if the first lot of eggs set are found to contain a large percentage of unfertiles it will be necessary to change the male, though a better plan will be to make sure at the commencement that the cockerel is vigorous and active in performing his functions. Only good-sized, well-shaped eggs should be set, and the procedure in hatching is so simple and so well known that we need only state that sitting hens should be fed and watered every day, being taken off the nest for from ten to fifteen minutes, and at any time after the eighth day the eggs may be tested before a strong light, when those containing live embryos will appear opaque, except for a well-defined air chamber at the large end.

The hatching period for hens' eggs is twenty-one days, and as soon as the chickens are dry they may be moved with the hen to a coop, measuring about 2ft. 3in. square, with a slatted front and a boarded floor well littered with peat moss, without which litter they would be very liable to suffer from cramp. March and April are the best months for hatching pullets to lay in the autumn, and as at that time of the year some nice weather is generally experienced the coops should be wired off as a run, or, failing that, a small covered run should be attached to the coop, with plenty of litter on the floor. Where space is very limited the latter plan is preferable, as it is easier to preserve cleanliness and prevent fouling in such a run.

Young chickens require feeding every two hours, and for the first two days it is advisable to give hard-boiled egg and breadcrumbs, for which purpose the unfertile eggs may be saved. Afterwards they may have two feeds a day of soft food, consisting of scalded breadcrust dried off with such meal as can be obtained, together with small wheat or other grain. Care must be taken to avoid giving too much, so that food is left lying about to become fouled and stale, which is a fruitful cause of diarrhoea. It must also be remembered that green food is absolutely essential, and for the first few weeks, until the birds are able to peck and help themselves from a cabbage hanging in the run, it is advisable to give lettuce or young cabbage leaves chopped up into small pieces and served either alone or with the soft food every day. Small grit must also be provided, and, of course, a constant supply of pure water.

Until the birds are weaned from the hen, which may be about the age of six to eight weeks, according to the state of the weather and the feathering of the chickens, the process of rearing in confinement or on intensive lines goes on much the same as usual, except that the birds are kept confined to limited sheltered quarters, and get their exercise mainly by scratching, whilst green food and other necessaries are provided.

With ordinary care and cleaning out of the coop litter about every fortnight and of run litter every three or four weeks, the young birds will make good progress. When their time comes to be drafted to separate quarters, however, it is no use putting them into a small bare open run with a roosting house. Such a run quickly becomes fouled, and nothing prejudices chicken growth more than foul ground; whilst there are no facilities for exercise in a small bare run. If sufficient space is available an open run may be provided as an adjunct to the covered run; but when space is very scarce it is advisable to have it all covered over and to work practically on the intensive system, with well-littered floor and all necessaries found. As we have said, it is much more costly than the full range system, as every bit of food—even green stuff—has to be provided; but so long as ordinary care is taken to keep the birds eager for food, to preserve cleanliness, and to keep the quarters airy and well shaded in summer, the birds will develop at a satisfactory rate. They must not be coddled in stuffy roosting houses, and as soon as they are well feathered in the spring they should be encouraged to sleep in open-fronted buildings. The scratching runs must be well lighted, but shaded in hot weather; green food must always be hung up within reach, grit and water kept handy, and corn must be thrown down to encourage scratching the same as for hens, whilst soft food must be served in troughs, and as the birds grow and the season advances the proportion of proteids should be increased in the form of pea meal and fish meal, so long as these materials do not encourage precocity and bring the pullets on to lay at an early age. This is one of the details that can only be learned by experience. It must also be remembered that as the birds grow they take up more room, so that it is very desirable to weed out the cockerels for table purposes as early as possible, and under favourable conditions it will be found that some of the birds will be in nice plump condition for killing at about the age of fourteen weeks, when they will fetch good prices as spring chickens. These small birds may not be very satisfying for a family; but it must be borne in mind that the cost of production is comparatively low, and, as space is valuable, it is questionable whether it is good policy to attempt to raise large table birds on these lines, especially when the main purpose is to rear healthy, vigorous pullets for laying purposes.

CHAPTER V

COUNTING THE COST

HAVING read thus far, and having decided that the advice given can be put into practice, the reader will be wondering what it will cost to become his own egg-producer. Some will assume that after paying the bill every egg they produce will cost something like a shilling; but let it be stated that even under present conditions, when prices are up all round, there is no reason why a householder with a small flock of hens should not produce eggs more economically than he can buy them—if such commodities are to be bought. The only serious items of expenditure are for the accommodation and for the stock, though in connection with the former item it may be possible to utilise an outhouse, or even a small greenhouse that is not required for any other purpose. If you are in any doubt about converting an outhouse into a poultry house you cannot do better than consult a local poultry-keeper who has had some experience, which reminds us that under the Domestic Poultry-keepers scheme local clubs are being formed, membership of which would entitle you to advice and guidance as well as close association with fellow poultry-keepers. If there is no such club in your locality write to the

Domestic Poultry Keepers Council, 55, Whitehall, London, S.W.I.

Remember that money spent on poultry houses and other plant need not be regarded as dead loss. A well constructed poultry house should last for years, especially if you give the timber a dressing with creosote every summer; so the best plan is to deduct a sum each year for deterioration, so that you can show the actual value in your balance sheet. Nor is the money spent on stock to be shown only as an item of expenditure—unless the birds should die; for after a year's production a hen has a killing value. You can keep her for two years' laying, and her carcass will still have a market value.

For his own satisfaction every poultry-keeper should adopt a simple method of keeping accounts, for that will add to the interest of the venture. On the debit side he will record all expenditure on foods and incidentals; and when he comes to make up his balance sheet at the end of the year he will have to charge for a year's use of the plant and the stock by putting down the difference between the original expenditure and the value at which it stands in his books when the year's accounts are made up.

No poultryman, be he commercial farmer or domestic keeper, can afford to neglect the health of his stock. Not only is it in his own interests to maintain a high standard of hygiene, but it is his duty to the public. Birds in full health produce the maximum number of eggs, unhealthy birds do not, and the country needs every egg it can get. To this end, Deosan Limited have devised the Blue Label Routine for poultry health and hygiene. Blue Label Deosan is a non-poisonous germicide and disinfectant.

Colds, snuffles and catarrh probably cause more loss in egg production than any other single factor. These conditions can be spread through the drinking water and water-borne infection can be effectively guarded against by the addition of this disinfectant to the drinking water. Moreover, it is beneficial to the general health of the birds. Incidence of air-borne disease can be greatly reduced by spraying the birds and their houses with Blue Label Deosan.

The Deosan Manual of Poultry Diseases, written by a Veterinary Surgeon Poultry Specialist, contains up-to-date and authentic information on all matters of poultry welfare; this booklet may be obtained free by application to Deosan Limited, Department K, 345, Gray's Inn Road, London, W.C.I.

We have said that anyone who goes about poultry-keeping in the right way should be able to make it pay. We will not venture to say how much profit can be made because it depends upon so many circumstances. But we must stress that while the present shortage lasts production of eggs for home consumption is a stronger incentive than profit. And here let it be stated that it is more important to acquire pullets that will lay plenty of eggs than to buy them at the lowest possible cost. It is true that there are pitfalls for the unwary in the purchase of livestock, and one of the advantages that should be derived from the poultry-keepers' clubs now being formed is that they should enable many beginners to obtain valuable guidance in the delicate task of buying pullets.

Everyone likes a good bargain; but remember that in buying poultry for laying, the best bargains are not necessarily the lowest-priced birds. We cannot advise you what to pay because prices fluctuate according to circumstances. Just now they are very high, because the demand exceeds supply; but whatever the standard rate remember that it is generally cheaper in the long run to pay a relatively high price to secure genuine pullets of laying capacity, provided you can be certain of what you are buying. More failures have resulted through buying inferior stock on the supposition that they were a better bargain than from any other cause, unless it is that so many beginners acquire late-hatched pullets and expect them to start laying in the autumn. So remember that heavy breed pullets should be hatched about Mid-March, and light breed pullets early in April; in which case you can, with good feeding and management, expect eggs early in October, and onwards throughout the winter.

times a day, and kept clean. See, also, that the troughs or vessels in which the food is served are kept clean; for though hens will eat most things when served up attractively their appetite may be spoiled by soured food.

The above is a general outline of feeding to-day; and as conditions vary considerably now it may be necessary or desirable to vary the methods. We know that for years to come there will be a scarcity of grain and meals, so that we must improvise as well as we can. But many of us realise that our present experiences will stand us in good stead in the future, when, though grains and meals may be available, we shall know that less costly materials will suffice to produce eggs.

Printed in Poland
by Amazon Fulfillment
Poland Sp. z o.o., Wrocław